I Am Proud of My Ancestors

They Overcame

I Am Proud of My Ancestors: They Overcame

ISBN: 9781949109580
Library of Congress Control Number: 2020949477
Printed in the United States
Anchor Book Press, Ltd
440 W. Colfax Street, Unit 1132
Palatine, IL 60078

I Am Proud of My Ancestors

They Overcame

Ama Oforiwaa Aduonum Ph.D.
Illustrated by Kojo Kisseh Aduonum

Anchor Book Press · Palatine

Table of Contents

Chapter I
ROOTS

My Ancestors were Enslaved
I am Proud
Do you know the story of my Ancestors
Do you know from whence they came
Listen to the tribute
A true report of injustice and adversity
Evidence of their strength and bravery

You may not know
I come from a long line of proud people
Of kings, of queens, of ordinary citizens
Beautiful women and men
Proud people and wise folk
From Africa they came
My soul runs deep
Hah

Do you know about Africa - Let *me* tell you
Africa is so BIG

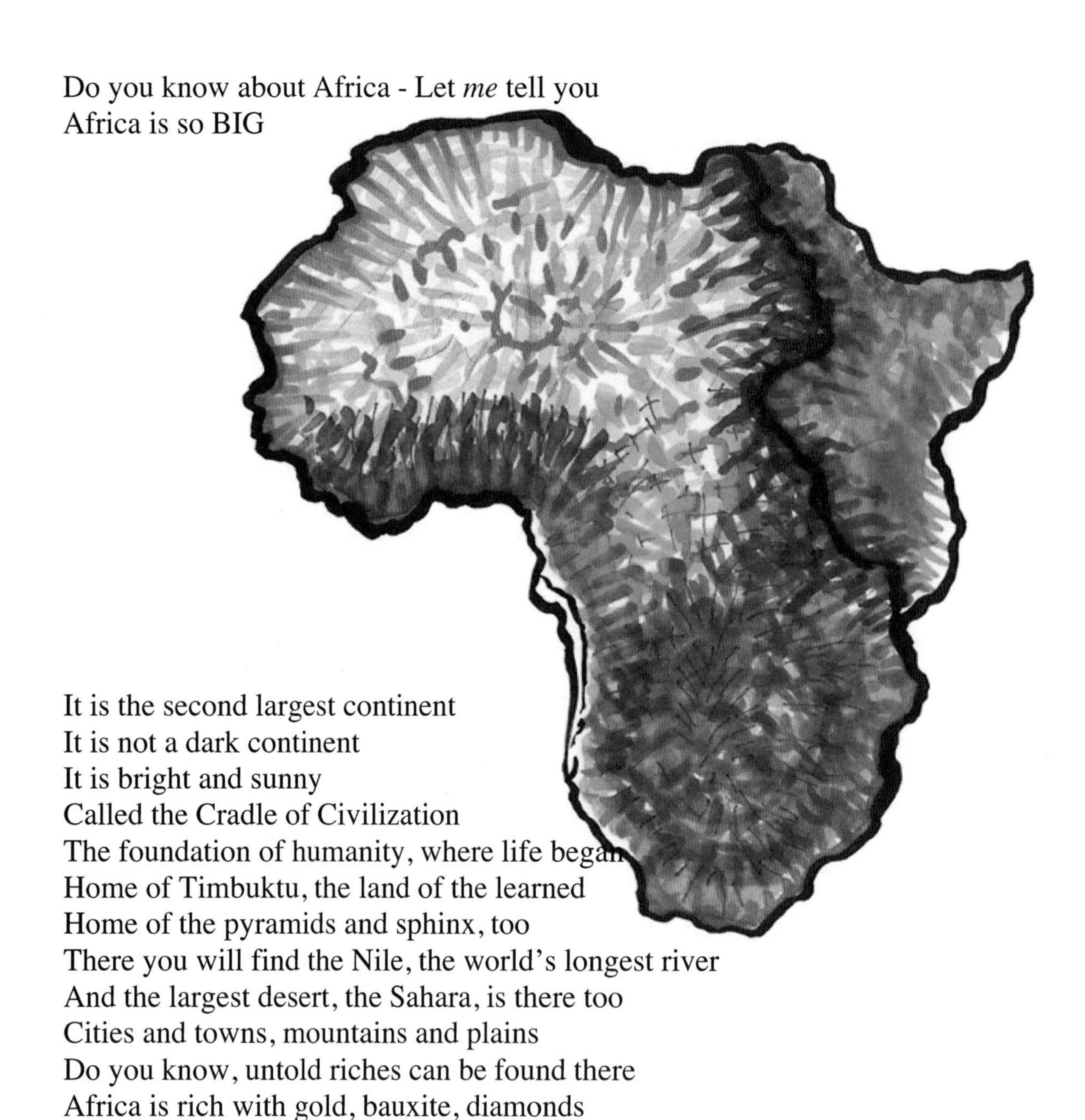

It is the second largest continent
It is not a dark continent
It is bright and sunny
Called the Cradle of Civilization
The foundation of humanity, where life began
Home of Timbuktu, the land of the learned
Home of the pyramids and sphinx, too
There you will find the Nile, the world's longest river
And the largest desert, the Sahara, is there too
Cities and towns, mountains and plains
Do you know, untold riches can be found there
Africa is rich with gold, bauxite, diamonds

Africa, the land of many empires
Songhay, Mali, Ghana
Great Zimbabwe, Kongo, Kush
Mutapa, Zulu, Yoruba, Ganda
Just to name a few

Like Africans today, My Ancestors spoke many languages
Wolof, Akan, Bulsa, Luo, Kikongo, Ga, Kimbundu, Igbo
More than can be told - Two, three, four, and even more
A sign of my Ancestors' intelligence
My Ancestors were Africans
Intelligent Africans
Clever and smart from the start

They did *not* call themselves tribes
They are Akan, Ganda, Yoruba, Shona, Mande, Bambara, Zande
Ewe, Xhosa people - And many, many more

Like my Ancestors, I love music
Africans sing and dance to bring the rains
To summon their Ancestors, or welcome the newborn
To Celebrate a child becoming an adult
To Celebrate life and to celebrate death
They sing to protest, to advise, to educate
They sing to instill pride
Africans play many instruments
Instruments that speak the humanity of the people
Instruments that speak the soul of the people
Drums, kora, mbira, xylophone, flutes

Combining beautiful melodies and sweet harmonies with complex rhythms
To talk, to summon, to compete, to mourn
To soothe, to grieve, to persuade, to warn
Talented people - I sing loud, I am Proud

My Ancestors loved soul food, too
Many flavorful recipes I am told
Herbs for tasty dishes
Herbs to strengthen their bones and muscles
To feed the mind, the body, the soul
Soul food by soul people
For my soulful Ancestors
In Africa
My Ancestors were warriors and storytellers
They told many stories
Stories to teach the importance of community responsibility
Respecting our elders and working hard
Seeking wisdom and integrity
Loving and supporting one another
Stories about consequences
Of procrastination, of greed, of selfishness

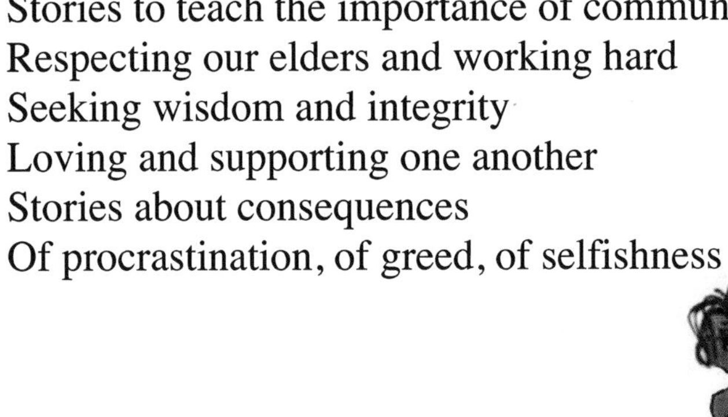

My Ancestors were the keepers of traditions
Preachers and healers, mothers and fathers
Inventors and farmers, artists and activists
They taught their children through the stories they told
Children just like me, just like you

Africa is a land of beauty
My Ancestors were beautiful
Beautiful Africans - Just like *you* and *me*
They were strong, bold, and alive
Hm!

Do you know where I got my good looks
My bright eyes and round nose
My sharp ears and big, thick lips
Nappy hair, wooly, kinky, tightly coiled hair

Yes, you guessed right
I am what my maker intended
Make no mistake
Just like the calves follow their mother
The young antelope leaps where its mother has leapt
I follow the ways of My Ancestors
I am made in the image of my beautiful parents
My beautiful Ancestors
I am black and beautiful! I am proud

From my Ancestors I have
Sharp, round ears to listen and hear
Round, flat, and spread out nose
So that I can breathe, take in all the air I need
Big, thick lips, to eat the food I love, good soul food
Mmmmm, yum

Nappy, kinky hair
To crown my head
Like royalty
Nappy hair
Designs my skull
Warming my skull
Coily and curly,
Moving in circles
Representing life
And energy

Hair!
Our hair needs food to grow, hair food
Thick hair oil, pomade, grease, *nkuto*, shea butter
To nourish, massage, and feed my hair
Beautiful styled braids, plaits, cornrows, bantu knots
Halos, puffs, fro hawks, waves, wrapped, or dreadlocks
Our hair is so stubborn and independent, just like me
If you try to straighten it, relax it, flatten it
It will resist and go right back to its coiled roots - Home
It has a mind of its own, just like me
R-E-S-P-E-C-T the naps, R-E-S-P-E-C-T me!

Did you know that we are the only ones on this earth
Black people, people of African descent
With nappy tightly coiled wooly hair
Unique and special – Hah
It needs special time and pampering
Our sophisticated, unflappable naps
Unlimited, imaginative styles
Beautiful hair from My Ancestors

You see - Their spirit lives in me
Their blood flows in you and me
We are joined in blood
My soul runs deep
I am *so* thankful! I am proud

Chapter II
TRANSITIONS

My Ancestors have suffered so
They were captured, kidnapped; sold to the highest bidder
Branded with hot irons; shackled in chains – no way to escape

They were marched hundreds of miles
Through tunnels and woods for weeks
Dehydrated, hungry, tired
They walked a lot, until they were numb
Sore feet, swollen feet, blistered feet
Sad, scared, terrified, weak, and weary

And still they marched, and marched, and marched
Leaving behind mothers, fathers, friends, and family
Leaving behind recipes, songs, dances, their community
Bringing stories to be told, creating history through their suffering

Though forced and tortured, many survived
They were held captive in dark and damp dungeons
Underground - below sea level
Some of them got sick, very sick
Moaning and groaning with no relief
Many rebelled, fought to get free

Some of them died, but many survived
You see
My Ancestors were strong; they suffered injustice and cruelty
They worked through adversity to survive

Marched through
The door of no return
They were packed tightly
In boats like sardines
For maximum profit, greed
Into the hulls of ships
They were chained

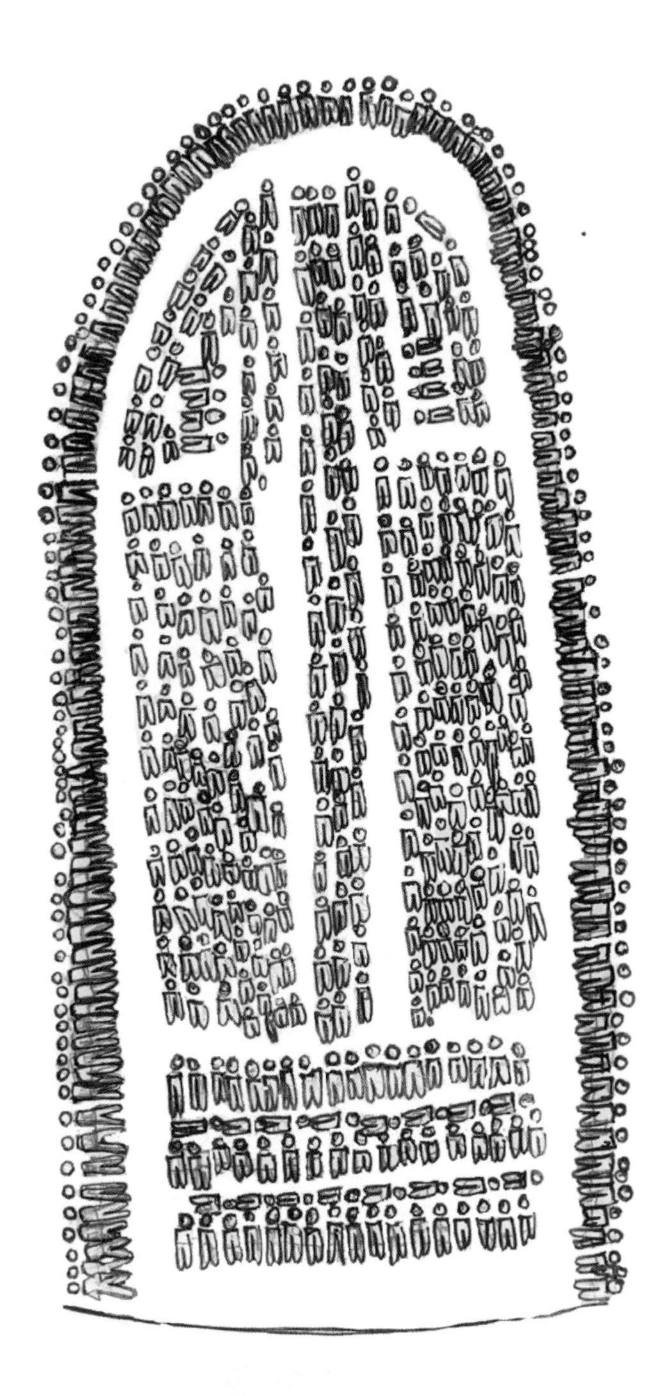

Taken by force
From Africa
To the Americas
Across the Atlantic Ocean
The suffering was not over
Forced to dance
On the decks of boats
To exercise and keep fit
Forced to make music
To entertain white enslavers
Smeared with palm oil
To appear healthy

Across the Atlantic Ocean
They were shipped
Never to return to Africa
Never to see again
The home that they loved

Imagine their shock in America, horrors anew
From tropical climate to temperate
Hot to warm and even cold
Seeing and experiencing snow for the first time
Snow

Different clothing, strange foods, favorite foods no more
Religious freedom a thing of the past
Even a new language, a new way of living

Imagine the nightmares
Unanswered questions filled their heads
Cut into the soul, how did they sleep
What did they tell their children
How did they survive, I do not know, but …
My Ancestors survived horrors untold
I will not forget their fight to survive
Of their survival, I am proud

My Ancestors determined to succeed, survived
They improvised and made things new
Created new food, new music, new language,
New ways of doing, of communicating
New ways of being

They formed communities
Supported each other, uplifted each other
Other mothers, other fathers cared for the orphans
They kept their heads up and kept moving

They were strong people, in mind, body, and soul
Back home in Africa they said
The bird that does not fly, stays hungry
So, they had to fly, they had to improvise
Improvise and make things anew
For their sanity, for their survival, they kept changing, moving forward
With the will to survive! I am proud!

In the Americas, My Ancestors helped build The New World
On this land, they labored and toiled
Invested their heart and soul, in this new land, America
With their sweat, blood, and tears, they survived and grew
I know this is true, I am proud

O, but My Ancestors worked hard
They worked on the plantations tilling, planting, harvesting, shucking
Making clothes from cotton
Cooking fine meals
For their enslavers
Women and men worked,
From sunup to sundown
Even children
Had no time to play
Working alongside parents
From sunup to sundown
Without pay
Just to survive
Just to avoid
The master's whip

All the while singing
Dancing and dreaming
Dreaming big dreams
Dreams of respect
Dreams of freedom
Dreams of equality
This land stands on the
Shoulders of my Ancestors
My Ancestors were strong
They overcame adversity
You bet, I am proud

They endured, unspeakable suffering
They were beaten, haunted, hunted
By white slave patrols
Hound dogs set on their trail

Lashed at the pole
Families were sold
Separated on the auction block
Fathers, mothers, children torn from each other's arms
Shhhhh!!!
Too many horrors
Unspeakable acts
Trauma, that cannot be told
I cry for their suffering

Yet, they survived, I am proud

You ask
How did they survive
They resisted and insisted on their humanity
They fought back, they rebelled
They waded in the water
Followed the drinking gourd
Followed designs stitched on quilts
Towards the North Star
To Freedom
Stole away from the master to their Maker
Hah

They sang work songs with directions to freedom
While they labored in the fields hey hollered to communicate to others
To express their anguish they wailed and mourned
They moaned and groaned for their emotional justice
For their freedom, for their humanity, they dared to demand freedom
They found the way to freedom! I am proud

They sang, speaking to the world, singing and testifying
The souls of my Black folk
Giving instructions for escape to a better place
"Wade in the water" and *"Steal away"*
"Run Mary, run, you've got a right to the tree of Life"
Fighting their enslavement, they sang

They sang
"Swing Low, Sweet Chariot" and *"There is a Balm in Gilead"*
Songs signifying hope and deliverance

They sang
"Old house, tear it down"
"Before I'd be a slave"
"I'd be buried in my grave"
To resist and defy their enslavement
To rebel against cruelty
Determined to reach their freedom
They sang of the way to be free. Yeah, I am Proud!

Do you know, the truth is told
The educated Black person was a threat, for education led to freedom's door
So, learning to read, to write was a crime in their time
Defying injustice, through secrecy, cleverness, and wit
They learned to read and write
They would not stay down, they challenged the law
The idea that said they were not intelligent
They outsmarted the unjust system with their wisdom
They were brilliant, unstoppable
On a roll

See
My Ancestors were strong and determined
They overcame adversity
They learned to read and write, I am proud

You know, My Ancestors were soldiers too
They defended this land. They fought, bled, and died for this land
They fought in the Revolutionary War for America's Independence
They fought in the Civil War to end their enslavement, to save the Union
They fought in all the other American wars, too
They died, were maimed and traumatized
They sacrificed their lives for the American Dream
They continued to fight, for their freedom and justice
For your freedom and mine

Soldiers in uniform, through it all, they kept their heads up
My Ancestors were strong, they overcame adversity
Moving forward, fighting, singing, looking ahead
Free at last
Free at last
Hey-ba!

We Celebrate Juneteenth, an American celebration
June 19th of each year
To honor the end to racialized slavery on June 19, 1865
For all My Ancestors, here is our Juneteenth Flag
See why I am Proud

Chapter III
REINVENTIONS

You see
My Ancestors were forced here
Against their will, in shackles and chains
Yet, they couldn't be held down
They would move mountains to be free
Reinvent themselves to triumph
Create a world for themselves

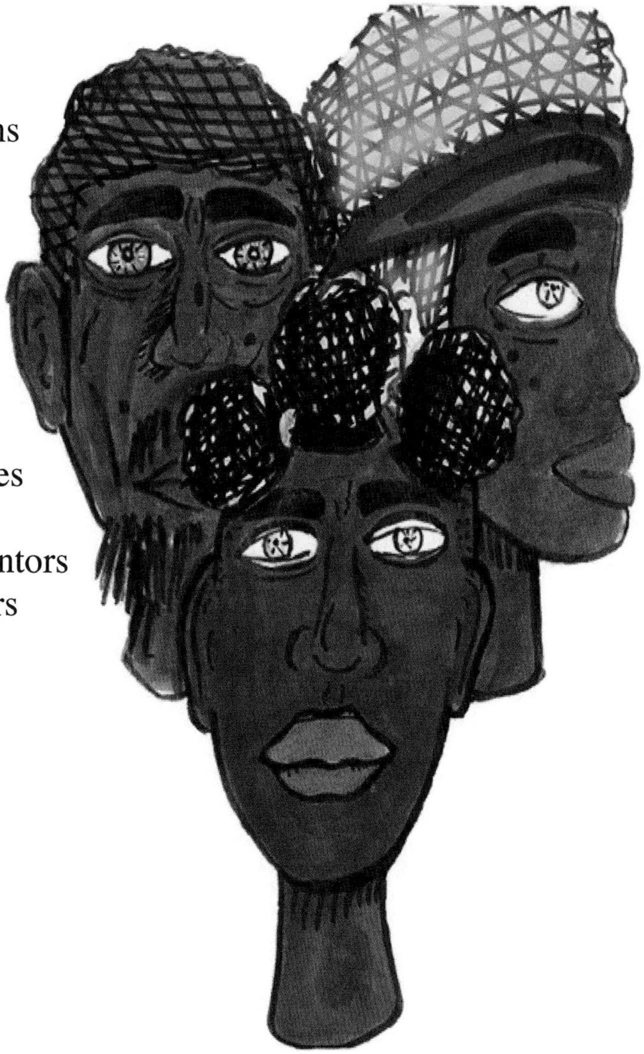

Becoming politicians, musicians, athletes
Lawyers, activists, scientists, teachers,
Warriors, artists, mentors, doctors, inventors
Philosophers, mothers, fathers, preachers
And more
Smart and famous
Remembering all, I am proud

My Ancestors were frontiersmen
Settling new lands in the West
Areas they were free to attain
They developed "Black Wall Street"
A successful economic district
In Tulsa, Oklahoma
They thrived in towns like Rosewood
Burnt to the ground by an angry mob

Still My Ancestors continued to fight
For their freedoms and rights
Freedoms and rights, we all enjoy
Standing tall, I am proud

You might know a few of their descendants
Like Dr. Martin Luther King Jr and Malcolm X
Rosa Parks and President Obama
Harriet Tubman, Nat Turner, and Sojourner Truth
Booker T. Washington founded a school—Tuskegee Institute
I am sure you read about them in school
My Ancestors say
"When the one who does not know studies,
The one learns"

So study to learn of others
Colin Powell worked with
Presidents Bush and Clinton

W. E. B. Du Bois started the NAACP
Madam C. J. Walker made products
For our beautiful hair
She was the first Black woman millionaire

Bold Maria Stewart was
The first feminist, black or white
She was a powerful speaker and abolitionist
A writer and a women's rights activist

Brave Ida B. Wells traveled the world
She refused to give up her seat on the train
Setting the stage for my Rosa Parks

My Ancestors pioneered in many areas
Surgeon Dr. Daniel Hale Williams performed the first successful open-heart surgery
There are many more scientists who changed the world
My Bessie Coleman was the first black female aviation pilot
They all led the way for me. I am proud!

I can also follow in the footsteps of
Matthew Alexander Henson, the 1st to reach the North Pole
Or Shirley Chisholm, the first Black woman in Congress
In 1972, she even ran for President

You know My Ancestors were creative like you and me
They created new music, new language, new art
Style, fashion, swag
New recipes from leftovers
Resourcefulness

When the drums were taken away
They made the guitar wail and moan
Work songs and spirituals
When dancing was banned
They shuffled and stepped
In perfect rhythm, patted the juba
Foot tapping, thigh slapping, handclapping
Flat foot dance
My Ancestors could not be held down
They overcame adversity
They were creative like that

Their descendants called themselves
The New Negro
Blues people
Soul people
My Ancestors ushered in the Black Renaissance
Making all that jazz
Beating injustice to the curb
Always with a swag

I will tell you and everyone
Loud and clear
I am proud

Do you like sports, music, dance, or theater
Do you play an instrument, sing, dance, or draw
My Ancestors did all of that too
You may have heard the song, *Hound Dog*
My Big Mama Thornton sang it first
Paul Robeson, Marian Anderson, Sissieretta Jones sang opera

Nina Simone talked about me when she sang
To Be Young, Gifted, and Black
Mahalia Jackson and Sister Rosetta Tharpe
Sang of our spirituality and faith in our Maker

Like their African Ancestors
Their descendants played many instruments

Did you know
Frederick Douglass played the violin
Othar Turner played a fife and in a drum band
Louis Armstrong mastered the trumpet and scat
So did Valaida Snow, Clora Bryant, Ernestine 'Tiny' Davis
In their hands, instruments sang, wailed, and moaned
I tell you, that is talent! Excellence! I am proud!

Do you like to play ball, run track, or box? My Ancestors did that too
Joe Louis and Muhammed Ali boxed anguish to the curb
Althea Gibson and Jackie Robinson set records playing ball
Alice Coachman jumped for Olympic Gold
Jesse Owens broke track records at home and abroad
Black bodies, athletic and strong
Winners of the game around the world

If you like art you may know
Aaron Douglass and Romare Bearden
Augusta Savage and Elizabeth Catlett
They painted and they drew
They wrote and they spoke
They sculpted and carved
To celebrate our culture
Our beauty, our pride
Our history, our politics, our community

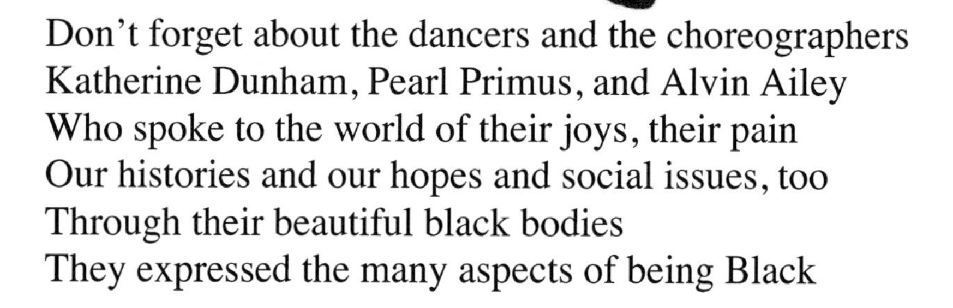

Don't forget about the dancers and the choreographers
Katherine Dunham, Pearl Primus, and Alvin Ailey
Who spoke to the world of their joys, their pain
Our histories and our hopes and social issues, too
Through their beautiful black bodies
They expressed the many aspects of being Black

Who could forget Pac, Biggie, Juice Wrld, the Last Poets
XXXTENTACION, Chynna Rogers, Lexii Alijau
Those warrior rappers hipped and hopped
The consciousness of my people declaring Black lives matter
And that's a fact. I am Proud

You see, My Ancestors' creativity and aspirations were beyond boundaries
Many people have tried to imitate them
They still continue to try to copy our creativity
Our swag, our cool
But like we say, "If you ain't got it, you just ain't"

They accomplished all they set their minds to
They lifted every voice and sang with swag, style, confidence, and pride
Nothing and nobody could hold them down
Hands down, I am proud!

Chapter IV

WORD: I AM PROUD!

CLASS
OF
20
20

My Ancestors gave me Intelligence, Beauty, Courage and Pride
The will to survive
Love for myself, love for others

I AM
Young, talented, and black
I AM My Ancestors' wildest dream
For their children to succeed
I will succeed. I am proud!

I am going to stay alive
I will *be* a legend
I will Live
Life is worth living
Everything is possible with life

My Ancestors were strong
They overcame adversity
So do not underestimate me
Their blood flows in my veins
I am young, black, and talented
I will survive
My life matters
I will LIVE

I will continue the work of my Ancestors
Making them proud
I am going to create
I am going to invent
Hold my head up high

I am going to love myself
Love my people justly
I will be my sisters' keeper
I will be my brothers' keeper
Respect my elders
Support my people

Hard times will not keep me down
My African Ancestors say
If the bird does not fly, it stays hungry
I will soar like the bird
I will challenge myself and prosper
Look at me
I stand tall with pride

I am somebody, I am black
Unapologetically bl—ack
Yes!
I am more than my hair
I am more than my skin
Dark skin, tar baby, high yella, red bone
Brown skin, many shades-like the rainbow
I'm black and proud

My African Ancestors say
The one who does not know, knows by learning
I will educate myself and seek knowledge
I will take control of my ideas
My thoughts, My knowledge
Claim my past, Know my history, Proclaim my future
I choose to learn,
I was born learning
I choose Me
I will choose to be proud

I will be more than an athlete or a rapper
More than a teacher or a scientist
I can be any of them, or I can choose to be a
Politician, surgeon, physician, an activist
Any career path I choose

It is important
That I choose to define who I am
Keeping my head up, I am black
Unapologetically bl—ack
My Ancestors sacrificed for me
They ran for freedom
So that you and I could walk
I will make them proud

You see
I am a proud and intelligent African American
My name is __________
I am Black and Proud
I will do me
Unapologetically Bl—ack!

I will not forget who my Ancestors are
I will not forget where I came from
Their blood runs in my veins
I'm not ashamed of my past
I will build on their sacrifices with pride
Their determination and strength
I will not disrespect Africa
I will learn about my African heritage
My soul runs so deep, I am proud!

Lest we forget, I am a Citizen of this America
This land is my land too
I am entitled to this land; I can go anywhere I choose
My Ancestors fought for this land
They gave me the right to be free
Fully entitled to this land, with freedom
Entitled to justice and tranquility
Blessings of Liberty for me and for my posterity
My rights! I am an American!
I am an unapologetically Bl--ack American!

I AM *We the People*. Created equal.
Endowed by my Maker with the same unalienable Rights
Life
Liberty
The pursuit of Happiness
Are my rights!
I too sing America, I am proud

I will continue to rise
Rise
Rise
Nothing is possible with defeat and fear
I will be unshackled
I will choose to rise
To succeed, My way
I choose to live free
To stand tall
Determined to have
My right to be free
I am free
I will choose

You know
My Ancestors were enslaved.
But My Ancestors were strong and determined
They overcame adversity
They fought against injustice
For me and for you
I am Black and proud

Look at me now
Evidence of My Ancestors' will to survive
Bright eyed and clear mind
Full of energy
Full of hope and brilliant ideas
The will to live
To change the world
I will make me a World for me

If you think my Ancestors were not determined
Look closely at me
Pay attention
I am determined
As My Ancestors were
Determined to live
With pride
With dignity and love
To change the world
I will follow their lead

I am proud to have African Ancestors
I am proud to be an African and an American
I am proud to be young and free
Proud to be Black
Intelligent
Alive
So proud to be me
Proud!!

Ancestors

1. The author is proud of her ancestors. List three things to be proud of.
   a. ______________________________
   b. ______________________________
   c. ______________________________

2. List three facts about Africa.
   a. ______________________________
   b. ______________________________
   c. ______________________________

3. The author lists physical features that are passed down to children. List three features from African Ancestors.
   a. ______________________________
   b. ______________________________
   c. ______________________________

4. All families pass down physical features. Choose another ethnicity and list 3 physical features passed down to children.
   a. ______________________________
   b. ______________________________
   c. ______________________________

5. List 3 ways all people are alike.
   a. ______________________________
   b. ______________________________
   c. ______________________________

6. List 3 Black Americans who were first (first millionaire, first on North Pole, etc.)
   a. ______________________________
   b. ______________________________
   c. ______________________________

7. List 3 Black American who made new discoveries in science and medicine.
   a. ______________________________
   b. ______________________________
   c. ______________________________

My Ancestors - Discussions

Ancestors are the people in our family tree. Everyone can look to the past to find out what their ancestors did to help the society we live in. Often we can look back at the struggles of our ancestors. It is said that our struggles can help build out character. What are some of the character traits the author talks about that were developed because of the struggles?

Think about transitions. In chapter 2, the author talks about transitions and how the ancestors' lives changed. What are some of the changes the ancestors made when they got to American?

One thing that all people have in common is the desire to be free. Even as a young person, you can understand those desires. One thing the author was proud of was that her ancestors did not give up as they fought for freedom. What are some of the things Black American did in the struggle to be free?

Chapter 3 is about successful Black Americans. Are there people in the book you did not know about? Who are the people you are most proud of? The book names just a few of the contributions Black Americans have made to this nation. How can you find out about others? How can you find out more about the people in this book?

The last chapter of the book talks about today. The ancestors had a wild dream that their children and their grandchildren would be successful. What will you do to be successful? Who can help you? How can you be strong when it seems the world is not on your side? How can you rise above what people do to keep you down?

"We hold these truths to be self-evident, that all men are created equal..." is a famous quote from our Declaration of Independence. Often these words are just read, without giving any real thought to them. But what does self-evident mean? Does the phrase 'all men' mean women are not included? You just need to glance around your class and see that everyone is different. How then are we created equal? If you keep reading the Declaration if Independence you see everyone has the right to Life, Liberty, and the Pursuit of Happiness. What does that mean?

My Ancestors-Vocabulary

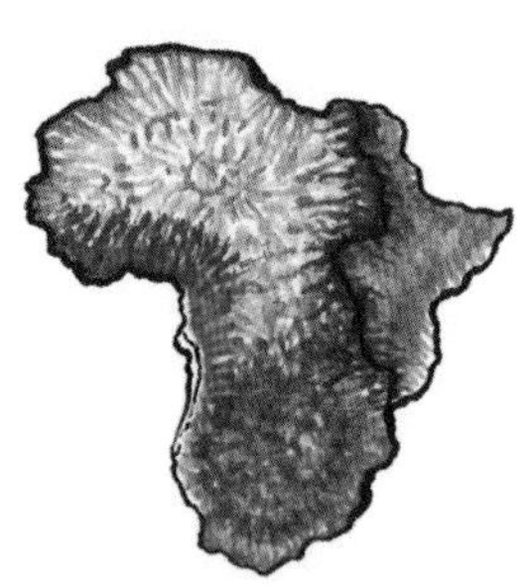

Definition	Draw Picture
adversity	
Sentence	Synonym

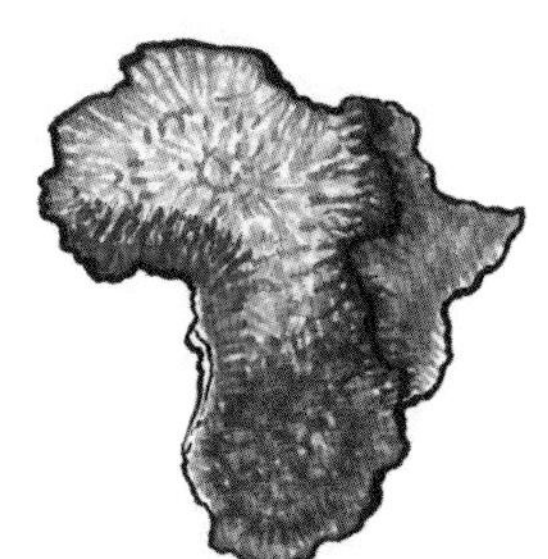

My Ancestors-Vocabulary

Choose your own word.

Definition	Draw Picture
Sentence	Synonym

My Ancestors-Glossary

adversity: a harsh and challenging condition that one has to overcome to move on

activist: person who works to bring change in a society

aspirations: goals, plans, or dreams

auction block: platform where items are exhibited, bided on, and sold

bidder: person who bargains or makes an offer to buy an item for sale

choreographer: person who creates or puts together different movements for a dance.

consciousness: state of being aware of your surroundings, the people and the world around you

consequences: result of an action one takes or a decision one makes

defy resist, reject, or disobey, especially, an order or law

deliverance: to be freed or rescued from a difficult situation

duplicate: to copy something

dungeon: underground spaces where enslaved Africans were stored; usually dark, cool, and damp

humanity: people, the human race

hulls: undersides of a ship or boat, often used to store items

imaginative: creative and original; it could be an artwork or idea

injustice: unfair practices that affect people negatively

maimed: to be hurt badly, usually involves a body part being damaged or lost

malleable: easy to bend or shape

NAACP: National Association for the Advancement of Colored People. W. E. B DuBois started this organization in 1909.

persist: to continue trying when it is difficult or look impossible

procrastination: pushing things back and promising to complete them at a later time

sophisticated: person who is stylish and classy

summon: to call or invite someone

temperate: areas in the world that have cold temperatures and sometimes, snow; areas can be found in northern parts of world

traumatized: to be hurt by an event whose impact stays with you for a long time

tribute: words spoken to celebrate a person's accomplishments

tropical: areas in the world with warm temperatures, often near the equator

unapologetically: to be who you are without asking permission from anyone, without apology to anyone

unflappable: unable or unwilling to change; people who are set in the ways, difficult to change their minds, especially if they are persistent.

wit: having the intelligence; using words in an inventive way to create humor

My Ancestors – Index

About the Author

©élan Studios

Ama Oforiwaa Aduonum is a nationally recognized playwright and performer whose solo performance of her art piece, *Walking with My Ancestors: Cape Coast Castle* (2019) has won national awards. Ama has a PhD from Florida State University and teaches courses in Black Music and Ethnomusicology. She also directs Ghanaian Drumming and Dance Ensembles and drum circles. She a Queen Mother in Ghana, *responsible for engaging youth as they move towards progress and success.*

As a researcher, writer, choreographer, performance artist, a storyteller, and a motivational speaker, Ama is *interested in both knowledge for its own sake and in using knowledge* to address issues in society. Her aim is to motivate others to accept and love themselves and help their communities. Ama enjoys cooking and spending time with her family in her spare time. She lives in the Midwest.

About the Illustrator

Kojo Kisseh Aduonum, a.k.a. Dark Chocolate, is a talented young artist, who has been drawing since he could hold a pencil at 2. He enjoys working with his 2 or 3 favorite mediums to create artwork. Kojo's career goal is to become an airline pilot. He plays mid-field on the soccer team; he also plays trumpet.

When he is not drawing, Kojo likes to skateboard, read comic books, listen to music, and play games with his family. He loves playing outside whether it is hot or cold. He loves roaming in the wilderness, when he gets a chance. Kojo lives in the Midwest with his family.

Printed in Great Britain
by Amazon

65545142R00033